POKÉMON ADVENTURES:
DIAMOND AND PEARL/
PLATINUM
Volume 4
Perfect Square Edition

Story by **HIDENORI KUSAKA**
Art by **SATOSHI YAMAMOTO**

© 2012 The Pokémon Company International.
© 1995-2012 Nintendo/Creatures Inc./GAME FREAK inc.
TM, ®, and character names are trademarks of Nintendo.
POCKET MONSTERS SPECIAL Vol. 4 (33)
by Hidenori KUSAKA, Satoshi YAMAMOTO
© 1997 Hidenori KUSAKA, Satoshi YAMAMOTO
All rights reserved.
Original Japanese edition published by SHOGAKUKAN.
English translation rights in the United States of America, Canada, the United Kingdom,
Ireland, Australia, New Zealand and India arranged with SHOGAKUKAN.

Translation/Katherine Schilling
Touch-up & Lettering/Annaliese Christman
Design/Yukiko Whitley
Editor/Annette Roman

Printed in the U.S.A.

Published by VIZ Media, LLC
P.O. Box 77010
San Francisco, CA 94107

10 9 8 7 6 5 4
First printing, February 2012
Fourth printing, June 2017

www.viz.com

Art
Satoshi Yamamoto

POKÉMON

ADVENTURES™

Diamond and Pearl

PLATINUM

Story
Hideno Kusak

Diamond

Pearl

A STORY ABOUT YOUNG PEOPLE ENTRUSTED WITH POKÉDEXES BY THE WORLD'S LEADING POKÉMON RESEARCHERS. TOGETHER WITH THEIR POKÉMON, THEY TRAVEL, DO BATTLE, AND EVOLVE!

SOME PLACE IN SOME TIME... THE DAY HAS COME FOR A YOUNG LADY, THE ONLY DAUGHTER OF THE BERLITZ FAMILY, THE WEALTHIEST IN THE SINNOH REGION, TO EMBARK ON A JOURNEY. IN ORDER TO MAKE A SPECIAL EMBLEM BEARING HER FAMILY CREST, SHE MUST PERSONALLY FIND AND GATHER THE MATERIALS AT THE PEAK OF MT. CORONET. SHE SETS OUT ON HER JOURNEY WITH THE INTENTION OF MEETING UP WITH TWO BODYGUARDS ASSIGNED TO ESCORT HER.

MEANWHILE, POKÉMON TRAINERS PEARL AND DIAMOND, WHO DREAM OF BECOMING STAND-UP COMEDIANS, ENTER A COMEDY CONTEST IN JUBILIFE AND WIN THE SPECIAL MERIT AWARD. BUT THEIR PRIZE OF AN ALL-EXPENSES PAID TRIP GETS SWITCHED WITH THE CONTRACT FOR LADY'S BODYGUARDS!

THUS PEARL AND DIAMOND THINK LADY IS THEIR TOUR GUIDE, AND LADY THINKS THEY ARE HER BODYGUARDS! DESPITE THE CASES OF MISTAKEN IDENTITY, THE TRIO TRAVEL TOGETHER QUITE HAPPILY THROUGH THE VAST COUNTRYSIDE.

Paka & Uji

THE REAL BODYGUARDS HIRED TO ESCORT LADY.

Sebastian

THE BERLITZ FAMILY BUTLER, WHO IS ALWAYS WORRYING ABOUT LADY.

Mr. Berlitz

LADY'S FATHER, WHO ASSISTS PROFESSOR ROWAN.

Professor Rowan

A LEADING RESEARCHER OF POKÉMON EVOLUTION. HE CAN BE QUITE INTIMIDATING!

Wave

A MASKED WRESTLER FROM PASTORIA.

Fantina

THE ALLURING SOULFUL DANCER OF HEARTHOME.

Maylene

THE ENTHUSIASTIC EAGER GYM LEADER AT VEILSTONE CITY.

Cynthia

THE MYSTERIOUS WOMAN WHO SOLVED THE CASE OF THE KIDNAPPED BIKE SHOP OWNER.

THE TWO BODYGUARDS ENTRUSTED WITH ESCORTING LADY ARE AWARE OF THE MIX-UP AND SET OUT TO CATCH UP WITH DIA, PEARL, AND LADY. TO TOP IT OFF, MYSTERIOUS TEAM GALACTIC IS BUSY MAKING TROUBLE IN THE SINNOH REGION. THEIR DEVIOUS PLAN IS TO CREATE A GALACTIC BOMB. WHAT WILL THIS STRANGE DEVICE DO?

NOW, TO RAISE MONEY FOR THEIR NEFARIOUS PROJECT, TEAM GALACTIC HAS SET THEIR SIGHTS ON THE WEALTHY BERLITZ FAMILY! PAKA AND UJI FINALLY CATCH UP WITH DIA AND PEARL, WHO HAVE JUST ARRIVED AT VEILSTONE CITY. THE MISUNDERSTANDING IS CLEARED UP, AND THE FOUR WORK TOGETHER TO PROTECT LADY FROM THE ENEMY. HOWEVER, IN THE MIDST OF BATTLE, PAKA AND UJI GET SWALLOWED UP BY A MYSTERIOUS SHADOW...!

Cyrus

TEAM GALACTIC'S BOSS. AN OVERBEARING, INTENSE MAN.

Galactic Grunts

THE TEAM GALACTIC TROOPS, WHO CARRY OUT THEIR LEADER'S BIDDING WITHOUT QUESTION. CREEPY!

Saturn

HE IS IN CHARGE OF THE BOMB AND RARELY STEPS ONTO THE BATTLEFIELD HIMSELF.

Mars

A TEAM GALACTIC LEADER. HER PERSONALITY IS HARD TO PIN DOWN.

Tru (Torterra, ♂)

RELAXED.
GOOD
PERSEVERANCE.

IMPISH.
LOVES TO EAT.

Lax (Munchlax ♂)

Chatler (Chatot, ♂)

HASTY.
SOMEWHAT
OF A CLOWN.

Chimler (Infernape, ♂)

NAUGHTY.
LIKES TO
RUN.

Ponyta (Ponyta, ♂)

MODEST.
OFTEN LOST
IN THOUGHT.

Empoleon (Empoleon, ♀)

SERIOUS.
A LITTLE QUICK
TEMPERED.

Dia's Pokémon

Pearl's Pokémon

Lady's Pokémon

POKÉMON

ADVENTURES
Diamond and Pearl
PLATINUM

④

CONTENTS

28

Crafty
Carnivine

12

GOOD JOB!

SIGH ...

IF YOU NEED A GRASS-TYPE POKÉMON THAT BADLY, WHY DON'T YOU JUST USE DIA'S TRU?

LIKE YOU USED MY CHIMLER BACK IN VEIL-STONE.

IN THE END, WE DIDN'T GET ONE POKÉMON OUT OF THE SAFARI GAME...

YEAH. SO FAR, WE HAVEN'T NABBED A SINGLE ONE.

I'M JUST GLAD WE ALL GOT OUT ALIVE...

FINE BY ME!

WOULD THAT BE OKAY?

YEAH. THE TOWN LOOKS SO PEACEFUL. I HAD NO IDEA.

THEY SHOULD'VE WARNED US HOW DANGEROUS IT IS HERE.

WAKE AND THE FOLKS AT PASTORIA WEREN'T VERY NICE.

AND SO WELL-MAINTAINED AND BEAUTIFUL...

IT REALLY IS PEACE-FUL.

AND IT'S ALL THANKS TO CRASHER WAKE!

INDEED IT IS, YOUNG LADY. PASTORIA IS A WONDERFUL PLACE FOR OLD FOLKS LIKE ME WHO AREN'T AS SPRY AS WE USED TO BE.

...HE PUTS TO USE TO HELP PEOPLE AND POKÉMON ALIKE.

WHAT HE EARNS FROM HIS BATTLES...

17

HOWDY!

HM? OH, IT'S YOU.

AGAIN.

SPLASH

WELCOME, YOUNG TRAINERS!

...**NOT** WHICH TWO THEY CHOOSE TO FIGHT WITH.

YOU'LL KNOW WHICH POKÉMON YOUR OPPONENT HAS ENTERED, BUT...

YOU ENTER THREE POKÉMON, THEN CHOOSE TWO TO TAKE TURNS IN BATTLE.

VERY WELL...I'LL EXPLAIN THE RULES.

YOU'RE FILTHY. I ALMOST DIDN'T RECOGNIZE YOU.

CLAN-CLAN-CLAN

WHOA!

OKAY.

DON'T JUMP TO CONCLUSIONS. PRESS THAT BUTTON FIRST.

THE GYM IS A WATER MAZE, BRIDGED BY FLOATING BARGES.

A MAZE, HUH? I DON'T SEE ANY WAY TO GET THROUGH IT EXCEPT BY SWIMMING!

... RAISING SUBMERGED STAIRS AND PATHWAYS.

AS YOU CAN SEE, PRESSING THE BUTTON CONTROLS THE WATER LEVEL...

18

...I KNOW TELLING YOU TO LEAVE WILL DO NO GOOD—SO GET IN THE BOAT.

WOO-HOO!

NOW THEN...IF YOU TWO WISH TO CHEER ON THE CHALLENGER...

IF YOU RUN INTO ANY OTHER GYM TRAINERS ALONG THE WAY, YOU MUST FIGHT THEM AS WELL.

AS WITH OTHER GYMS, YOUR BATTLE OPPONENT WON'T ONLY BE CRASHER WAKE...

THAT'S BECAUSE WE'RE GOING THROUGH THE MAZE. DON'T WORRY, WE'LL REJOIN HER SHORTLY.

HEY! WE'RE GETTING FARTHER AND FARTHER AWAY FROM LADY!

WAIT! WHAT THE ...?!

GOOD LUCK, LADY!

DON'T TELL ME YOU'RE LOST!

HUH? A DEAD-END!

MAYBE IT'S THIS WAY.

SHE'S FACING THE GYM LEADER ALREADY!

HEY, PEARL! LOOK!

HMM...

GREAT! WE'RE GONNA MISS LADY'S ENTIRE FIGHT!

NOW THEN! LET'S SHOW EACH OTHER THE BEST WE'VE GOT!

WHICH ONE WILL CRASHER WAKE CHOOSE FIRST?!

TWO OF THE THREE POKÉMON I ENTERED WILL FIGHT...

LET'S ADJUST THE RULES! FOR JUST THIS BATTLE, LET'S MAKE IT OKAY TO USE **ALL** THE WATERWAYS FROM HERE TO THE ENTRANCE!

I KNOW!

NOW THIS SMALL PARCEL OF LAND SEEMS TOO SMALL TO DO BATTLE ON!

WHAT?!

A FINE EMPOLEON!

OH HO! AHA HA HA HA!

IF YOU'RE UP FOR IT, THAT'S FINE. BUT I DISAPPROVE OF CHANGING RULES MIDWAY THROUGH!

WHAT DO YOU THINK...?

...

APOLOGIES. CRASHER WAKE LIKES TO RAISE THE STAKES. AND WE NEVER KNOW WHAT HE'S GOING TO COME UP WITH NEXT.

IS THAT EVEN ALLOWED?

HMM.

HE'S GOING TO CHANGE THE RULES—FOR JUST THIS FIGHT?!

LET THE BATTLE BEGIN!

CHARGE

KER-SPLASH

SLASH

TMP TMP TMP TMP

THEY LEFT THE BATTLE-FIELD...

...AND SWITCHED TO THE POOL!

BUT EMPO-LEON CAN OUT-SWIM A JET BOAT!

▼Info

🌀009 Empoleon
Emperor Pokémon
WATER STEEL

Height: 5'07"
Weight: 186.3lbs

It swims as fast as a jet boat. The edges of its wings are sharp and can slice apart drifting ice.

▼Info

🌀057 Floatzel
Sea Weasel Pokémon
WATER

Height: 3'07"
Weight: 73.9lbs

It floats using its well-developed flotation sac. It assists in the rescues of drowning people.

ONE IS A SEA WEASEL POKÉMON WHO USES ITS FLOTA-TION SACK TO STAY ABOVE THE SURFACE AND ITS TAIL AS A PRO-PELLER!

◇ ADVENTURE MAP ◇

▶ Pastoria City ◀

Oreburgh VS Roark Coal Badge	Eterna VS Gardenia Forest Badge	Veilstone VS Maylene Cobble Badge					

DIAMOND

PEARL

▶ TRU
Torterra ♂

▶ LAX
Munchlax ♂

▶ CHIMLER
Infernape ♂

▶ CHATLER
Chatot ♂

▶ EMPOLEON
Empoleon ♀

▶ PONYT
Ponyta ♂

29

Floatzel
and
Jetsam

OH! FLOATZEL'S GONNA OVERTAKE EMPOLEON!

THEY'RE BOTH SO FAST!

NOPE ...

SPLASH

BO

NEXT!

GO!

AH-HAH! WELL DONE!

EMPOLEON LET FLOATZEL CATCH UP TO IT ON PURPOSE— TO GET IN RANGE OF VACUUM WAVE!

THUD

IT DID IT!!

SRONG

THE TWO POKÉMON THAT CRASHER WAKE CHOSE OUT OF THE THREE HE ENTERED WERE FLOATZEL AND QUAGSIRE!

FSHOOOOP

SPRAAAY

SPLAT

TALK ABOUT A LAID-BACK FIGHT.

THIS IS NOTHING LIKE THE LAST MATCH!

BLOOP BLOOP

TRU FELL IN!

AND LADY WITH IT!

HE'S WAITING FOR LADY TO COME UP SO HE CAN ATTACK!

...BLIZZARD ATTACK!

HE'S GOING TO KNOCK TRU OUT OF THE GAME WITH ONE...

LADY! COME UP QUICK!

NO, DUMMY! LOOK AT CRASHER WAKE!

34

THE CHAL-LENGER WINS!

QUAG-SIRE IS DOWN FOR THE COUNT!

...I LEARNED TWO TRICKS FROM IT.

THE SAFARI GAME IN THE GREAT MARSH WAS A HARROW-ING EXPE-RIENCE, BUT...

LADY WON!

SHE WON!

NO WAYYYY!

And we missed it.

YOU CAN PINPOINT SOMEONE'S LOCATION UNDERWATER FROM THE BUBBLES OF AIR THEY RELEASE.

THE OTHER WAS FROM GETTING SUBMERGED UNDER THE WATER.

I LEARNED THE BENEFIT OF HIDING YOURSELF IN A FIGHT.

THE FIRST WAS FROM CARNIVINE.

WHAT DO YOU THINK, DIA?

I'M IMPRESSED! YOU TOOK ADVANTAGE OF A SETBACK TO DEPLOY A CLEVER TRICK!

...WHICH MASKED YOUR ESCAPE WHILE YOU TOOK OFF THROUGH THE CLOUDY WATER!

BUT THEY WERE COMING FROM YOUR OVERALLS...

WE THOUGHT YOU WERE RIGHT UNDER THE SPOT WHERE THOSE BUBBLES WERE COMING UP.

WOW, LADY!

THIS IS A POOL, NOT A BATHTUB!

PLUS, NOW SHE WON'T NEED TO TAKE A BATH!

SMACK

YEAH...

NOW THAT SHE'S CLAIMED HER VICTORY HERE AT THE PASTORIA GYM, IT'S WORTH HER GETTING SOAKING WET.

YEP. SHE'S VERY RESOURCEFUL. SHE TURNED A HANDICAP INTO AN ADVANTAGE!

SO THAT'S WHY SHE CAME STRAIGHT HERE STILL CAKED IN MUD...

...SOME PRIZE MONEY, RIGHT?

EVEN THOUGH I WON, YOU'LL STILL GET...

WHAT'S THAT, CHALLENGER?

I HAVE A QUESTION THOUGH.

BUT... WHY DO YOU ASK?

YES. PRIZE MONEY IS AWARDED JUST FOR FIGHTING A CHALLENGER. DON'T WORRY ABOUT ME.

IN THE HEAT OF BATTLE, I FORGOT ALL ABOUT IT. I JUST CONCENTRATED ON GIVING IT EVERYTHING I HAD.

NOT REALLY...

HA HA HA! I SEE. DID KNOWING THAT MAKE IT HARD FOR YOU TO FIGHT TO WIN?

WELL, I MET AN OLD WOMAN IN TOWN WHO TOLD ME THAT YOU SPEND YOUR PRIZE MONEY ON MAINTAINING PASTORIA CITY AND PROTECTING THE GREAT MARSH. SO...

I WANT YOU TO KNOW...

GOOD! THAT'S HOW A CHALLENGER SHOULD BE!

JUST SO YOU KNOW— THE OTHER LEADERS DON'T FIGHT LIKE HIM.

IT DOES.

THE ROAD LOOKS PRETTY STEEP.

WE NEED TO VEER WEST A LITTLE AND THEN NORTH TO FOLLOW THE ROUTE.

ALL RIGHT! LET'S MOVE ON!

LET'S GO!

ON TO MT. CORONET!

ADVENTURE MAP

▶ Route 212 ◀

Oreburgh VS Roark Coal Badge	Eterna VS Gardenia Forest Badge	Veilstone VS Maylene Cobble Badge	Pastoria VS Wake Fen Badge				

DIAMOND

PEARL

▶ TRU
Torterra ♂

▶ LAX
Munchlax ♂

▶ CHIMLER
Infernape ♂

▶ CHATLER
Chatot ♂

▶ EMPOLEON
Empoleon ♀

▶ PONYTA
Ponyta ♂

30

Suffering
Psyduck!

AS YOU CAN SEE...

POKÉMON MANSION...

ONCE POKÉMON EXPERIENCE THE GLORY OF MY TROPHY GARDEN THEY DON'T WANT TO GO ANYWHERE ELSE.

...MY MANSION AND TROPHY GARDEN ARE MY PRIDE AND JOY!

DIA? HOW LONG DO WE HAVE TO TOUR THIS GUY'S PLACE?

WISH I KNEW.

Psst

Psst

IT'S LOVELY!

IT'S LOVELY!

WOULD YOU LIKE TO VIEW MY PRIZE-WINNING GARDEN?

YES, PLEASE!

...MADE UP HER MIND TO BARGE IN.

WHAT A GORGEOUS BUILDING! MUST BE A HOTEL! WE'LL STAY HERE TONIGHT!

IT ALL STARTED WHEN LADY...

46

HEY, YOU!

WE VISITED TOO!

AS A MEMENTO OF YOUR VISIT TO THE ESTATE, PLEASE ACCEPT THIS SOOTHE BELL.

I SEE. GIVE OUR GUEST A PARTING GIFT.

MASTER, YOUR VISITOR IS HERE.

I WON'T!

DON'T TOUCH A THING!

ALL THE STATUES AND FURNITURE IN THIS MANSION ARE PART OF MASTER BACKLOT'S VALUABLE COLLECTION.

I'D LIKE TO INVES- TIGATE EVERY NOOK AND CRANNY OF THIS GARDEN. DO YOU MIND...?

PEARL? DIA- MOND?

I'VE GOT AN IDEA!

HM.

HEY, PEARL... IF YOU DON'T LIKE IT HERE, LET'S GO— JUST YOU AND ME.

HOW COME WE'RE GETTING TREATED SO BADLY ?!

THEN AGAIN...IT'S KIND OF A DRAG TO ALWAYS BE ON DUTY 24/7.

BUT WHAT IF SOMETHING HAPPENS TO LADY? I'D NEVER FORGIVE MYSELF! WE CAN'T LEAVE HER ALL ALONE.

UM...

CAUSE THE STAFF WASN'T NICE TO US!

THAT'S BARELY A PUN!

HUH?! WHY'S THAT?!

BUT IT'S NOT THAT NICE.

FULL OF POKÉMON.

POKÉMON MANSION IS AN INCREDIBLE BUILDING WITH A FINE GARDEN.

IF I DON'T SAY ANYTHING, HOW CAN I SAY A PUNCHLINE?!

IF YOU DON'T HAVE SOMETHING NICE TO SAY DON'T SAY...

HE WON'T STOP BRAGGING ABOUT HIS THINGS.

I DON'T KNOW...

THAT MR. BACKLOT GUY SURE IS GENEROUS TO LET TOTAL STRANGERS IN TO SEE HIS GARDEN.

THANKS FOR YOUR ACCOUNT OF THE PROBLEM, MR. BACKLOT.

YEAH.

THE COAST LOOKS CLEAR.

HEY!

OH!

OH!

I'LL HAVE TO LOOK INTO THIS FURTHER.

BUT FIRST, I'LL GO TO ROUTE 210...

HM?

CYNTHIA?!

IT'S YOU!

WHERE'S THAT GIRL THAT WAS WITH YOU?

I ALMOST DIDN'T RECOGNIZE YOU! YOU LOOK SO MUCH MORE MATURE AND INDE-PENDENT NOW!

OH! YOU TWO AGAIN!

REMEM-BER? YOU TAUGHT US SOME BATTLE SKILLS BACK IN ETERNA CITY.

OH, I SEE...

SO ONCE AGAIN ALL THREE EVOLVED AROUND THE SAME TIME AGAIN.

SHE'S LOOKING GOOD TOO.

WELL, YOU SEE...

PRO-CEED.

YOU DON'T MIND IF I TELL THEM, DO YOU?

ME? CONDUCTING AN INVESTIGATION FOR MR. BACKLOT.

WHAT ARE YOU DOING HERE, CYNTHIA?

YOU REALLY ARE GROWING STRONGER, ALL OF YOU.

BUT THERE WAS AN INCIDENT THERE RECENTLY.

IT'S A PLACE WHERE PEOPLE LIKE TO WALK THEIR POKÉMON, LIKE CLEFAIRY, PACHIRISU, AND PSYDUCK.

AND I'VE HEARD ABOUT THAT SQUARE.

WE'VE BEEN TO HEARTHOME!

MR. BACKLOT OWNS AMITY SQUARE IN HEARTHOME CITY.

OH!

SOMEONE LOST THEIR PSYDUCK.

DO YOU THINK... THOSE TWO INCIDENTS ARE RELATED?

I DO.

WE HAD TO TAKE A DETOUR EAST.

OH, YEAH! WE GOT STUCK THERE OURSELVES!

AND THEN, SHORTLY THEREAFTER, ROUTE 210 BECAME SO CONGESTED WITH PSYDUCK THAT PEOPLE COULDN'T GET THROUGH!

ZOOOM

HEH HEH!

WOW, YOUR GARCHOMP IS **FAST**, CYNTHIA. AND SO ARE YOU!

WHEEZE! WHEEZE! WE MADE IT!

SQUEAK

A TANK? AND SOME KIND OF HOSE?

THESE TWO ITEMS WILL COME IN HANDY.

IT'S FUN. I LOVED RIDING WHEN I WAS A KID. STILL DO.

WITH SUCH A FAST POKÉMON, HOW COME YOU RIDE A BIKE?

...THEY SHOULD BE JUST OVER THIS HILL.

NOW, IF NOTHING'S CHANGED...

I'LL USE IT AS AN IMPROMPTU DIFFUSER.

55

HOW CAN WE POSSIBLY SHIFT THIS MOB?!

A FLOCK OF PSYDUCK SUFFERING FROM MIGRAINES!

THERE THEY ARE!

...ALL THAT MATTERS IS CURING THEM.

BUT RIGHT NOW...

...NOBODY KNOWS WHAT CAUSES THEM.

PSYDUCK ARE KNOWN FOR HAVING MIGRAINES. UNFORTUNATELY...

YES. A LIQUID FORM OF THE POTION!

SO THAT TANK IS FILLED WITH—

A SECRET POTION!

WITH **THIS**!

LOOK UP AND SAY "AAAH!"

HEY, PSYDUCK!

LITTLE BY LITTLE ...

...EACH OF THEM IS MOVING ON ITS WAY.

THE PSYDUCK LOOK A LOT HAPPIER ALREADY.

I'M TOLD THAT'S THE DISTINGUISHING FEATURE OF THE PSYDUCK WHO WENT MISSING FROM AMITY SQUARE.

SEE HOW THIS PART TURNS IN A LITTLE?

OH! I SEE!

Missing: Psyduck

IT ISN'T JUST THE WILD ONES, BUT TRAINERS' PSYDUCK TOO, WHICH MEANS...

THIS CERTAINLY MAKES ONE THING CLEAR ...

THERE!

OH! UH, NOTHING...

WHAT ARE YOU THINKING, CYNTHIA?

...SOMEBODY GATHERED THEM HERE ON PURPOSE. TO KEEP SOMEBODY FROM...

YEAH. AND WE CAN GET TO MT. CORONET VIA THE NORTHERN ROUTE.

AT LEAST NOW ALL THE PEOPLE WHO WERE INCONVENIENCED WILL BE ABLE TO PASS THROUGH.

...GETTING THROUGH PERHAPS...

SEE CAFÉ CABIN OVER THERE?

CAFÉ CABIN

I SEE.

CELESTIC TOWN

MT. CORONET

PSYDUCK

CAFÉ CABIN

ACTUALLY, THIS WASN'T THE ONLY SIDE THAT WAS BLOCKED. SOME PEOPLE COULDN'T GET HERE FROM CELESTIC TOWN EITHER.

I'M RIGHT OVER HERE!

CYNTHIA!

SHE TRAVELS A GREAT DISTANCE TO GET IT. I BET SHE'S UPSET THAT SHE HASN'T BEEN ABLE TO COME HERE IN A WHILE.

MOO-MOO MILK!

MY GRANDMA LIVES IN CELESTIC. SHE LOVES THE MOOMOO MILK THEY SELL AT CAFÉ CABIN.

58

31

Problematic
Probopass
&
Mad
Magnezone I

URP! SEC-ONDS, PLEASE!

COM-ING RIGHT UP!

SPEAK-ING OF POKÉ-MON...

SPEAK-ING OF POKÉ-MON...

HMM...

NGH!

WHAT'S THE MATTER? START ALREADY!

THEN WE'LL PERFORM FOR HER—AS A GESTURE OF APPRECIATION. WHAT DO YOU SAY, PEARL?

SHE CAN TELL US THE LEGEND OF THE LAKES ON THE WAY.

I DUNNO...

WE OUGHT TO ACCOMPANY THIS ELDERLY LADY HOME TO CELESTIC TOWN.

LIKE YOU SAID, THE ROAD IS SO FOGGY IT WOULD BE DANGEROUS TO TRAVEL ALONE.

SHOW ME ANOTHER ROUTINE!

IMPORTANT... RIGHT...

THEY CALL HER THE TOWN ELDER BACK IN CELESTIC TOWN. SHE'S AN IMPORTANT PERSON.

AND REPORT BACK TO MR. BACKLOT.

I HAVE TO GET THIS PSYDUCK BACK TO AMITY SQUARE.

YOU'RE NOT COMING WITH US, CYNTHIA?

WELL, I HAD BEST BE GOING.

I'M OFF!

SEE YA!

BUT JUST IN CASE...I'LL LEAVE MY GARCHOMP WITH YOU.

YOU SHOULD BE FINE TRAVELING TO CELESTIC TOWN WITH MY GRANDMA.

YES, MA'AM!

BE SURE TO FOLLOW IN MY FOOTSTEPS EXACTLY.

WATCH YOUR STEP!

THE FOG GOT REALLY THICK REALLY FAST!

JINGLE
JINGLE

JING
JING

I'M WALKING WITH MY RINGING CHINGLING.

JINGLE
JINGLE

IF YOU CAN'T USE YOUR EYES, USE YOUR EARS.

!

WAIT, ELDER−!

JINGLE
JINGLE

I CAN'T SEE A THING!

JINGLE

SLIP

JINGLE

YEAH ...

BUT ...

JINGLE

I WISH THIS FOG WOULD GO AWAY.

I FEEL MORE DEAD THAN ALIVE.

THANKS, GUYS.

HA HA HA HA!

WAAAH!

GRA

DON'T SPEAK ILL OF THE FOG.

THEY'RE ALL NATURAL WONDERS THAT HAVEN'T CHANGED FOR EONS.

THE LAKES YOU'RE ALREADY FAMILIAR WITH...

THIS PATH, THE FOG, MT. CORONET...

THIS NATURAL PHENOMENA CAN ONLY BE FOUND IN THE SINNOH REGION.

...AND LAKE VALOR...

...LAKE ACU-ITY...

...LAKE VER-ITY...

SINNOH HAS THREE GREAT LAKES...

ESPE-CIALLY THE LAKES!

LOOK!

WAIT!

WHAT AN ATTACK! GARCHOMP'S CORNERING IT...SLOWLY BUT SURELY!

IT PRETENDED TO DODGE— TO USE GARCHOMP'S HYPER BEAM...

...TO OPEN UP THE CAVE!

OH NO! HE'S GOING INSIDE THE CAVE!

MAGNE-ZONE'S MIRROR SHOT DECREASED GARCHOMP'S ACCURACY.

THAT'S RIGHT.

...AND THE UNIQUE RELATIONSHIP BETWEEN THEM.

...THREE CREATURES AND THREE LAKES...

THESE DRAWINGS SHOW ...

I KNEW IT.

UXIE.

AZELF.

AND MESPRIT.

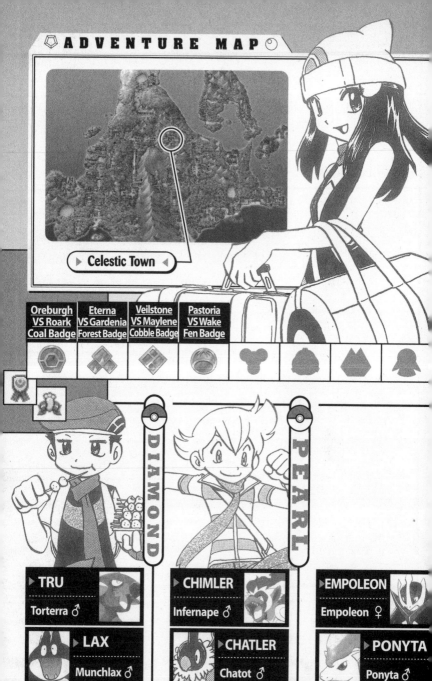

◇ADVENTURE MAP◇

▶ Celestic Town ◀

Oreburgh VS Roark Coal Badge	Eterna VS Gardenia Forest Badge	Veilstone VS Maylene Cobble Badge	Pastoria VS Wake Fen Badge				

DIAMOND

PEARL

▶ TRU
Torterra ♂

▶ LAX
Munchlax ♂

▶ CHIMLER
Infernape ♂

▶ CHATLER
Chatot ♂

▶ EMPOLEON
Empoleon ♀

▶ PONYTA
Ponyta ♂

32

Problematic
Probopass
& Mad
Magnezone
II

THAT MEANS HE'S SEEN THE WALL MURALS!

HE WENT INTO THE RUINS!

...NOBODY MUST EVER LAY EYES UPON THEM!

EVEN THOUGH ACCORDING TO OUR LEGEND...

I SEE.

HMM...

...CONTROLS EMOTION.

AND MESPRIT, WHO RESIDES IN LAKE VERITY...

...IN LAKE VALOR.

AZELF, WHO CONTROLS WILLPOWER, IS...

THAT'S UXIE.

THE ONE WHO CONTROLS KNOWLEDGE IS IN LAKE ACUITY...

HUH?

BUT IS IT JUST ME, OR...IS SOMETHING DIFFERENT THIS TIME?

YOU'RE WORRIED BECAUSE... HE'S WEARING THE SAME EMBLEM AS THE GROUP THAT WENT AFTER LADY BACK IN VEILSTONE, RIGHT?

WAIT, DIA!

GET DOWN, LADY. HE'LL SEE YOU!

OUTSIDE, ALL HE DID WAS BATTLE GARCHOMP. AND NOW HE ONLY HAS EYES FOR THAT MURAL.

...ANY INTEREST IN ANY OF US— LEAST OF ALL LADY.

THIS MAN DOESN'T SEEM TO HAVE...

IN OTHER WORDS, I THINK HE ONLY CAME TO CELESTIC TOWN TO INVESTIGATE THIS LEGEND!

...THIS MAN'S POSITION AND MISSION AREN'T THE SAME.

HE MIGHT BE FROM THE SAME ORGANIZATION, BUT...

WE RUN!

ISN'T IT OBVIOUS? HOW STUPID ARE YOU, DIA?

SO WHAT DO WE DO? FIGHT HIM?

HE HAS POKÉMON THAT OUR POKÉDEXES DON'T RECOGNIZE.

CYNTHIA'S GARCHOMP CAN'T MANEUVER FAST.

NOT TO MENTION THAT HE ALMOST BURIED US ALIVE BACK AT MT. CORONET!

THAT'S THREE REASONS WHY WE DON'T STAND A CHANCE IN A FIGHT WITH HIM!

ZAP

GRAWR!

AT THE VERY LEAST, WE CAN GET LADY OUT OF DANGER!

...WE HAVE A CHANCE TO RUN AWAY.

AS LONG AS THAT MAN ISN'T PAYING ATTENTION TO US...

TELL GARCHOMP TO GIVE US ALL A RIDE TO JUST OUTSIDE OF CELESTIC TOWN.

...PLEASE GIVE GARCHOMP SOME ORDERS FOR US.

ELDER! I KNOW YOU'D PREFER NOT TO, BUT...

HMPH!

...

3

2

1

LET'S GO, ELDER!

WE DON'T HAVE A CHOICE.

ZOOM ZOOM ZOOM

FLA

SPEED-ING ACROSS THE LAND! SOAR-ING ACROSS THE SKY!

POUND THE EARTH!

TAH-DUM DUM DUM DUM!

CHA CHA CHA CHA CHA!

IT'S MY FAVOR-ITE ROBOT SHOW.

DO YOU KNOW ABOUT PRO-TEAM OMEGA?

BEAT THOSE BAD GUYS DOWN, DOWN, DOWN!

COMBIN-ING TO BECOME PRO-TEAM OMEGA! TAKE DOWN THE DEMON BRIOCHE!

FASCINAT-
ING. NOW
IF I CAN
DETERMINE
HOW OLD
THESE
MURALS
ARE...

THAT'S
WHAT I'VE
DECIPHERED
FROM THESE
TEXTS.

WHEN
KNOWLEDGE
IS EXPANDED,
LIFE IS
ENRICHED.
WHEN
EMOTION
AWAKENS, JOY
AND SORROW
COEXIST. WHEN
A DECISION IS
MADE, ACTION
IS TAKEN.

HEY!

I'LL GO
BACK
TO MY
VEHICLE
AND PRE-
PARE
MY ANA-
LYZER.

92

TRU SHIELDED ME WITH WITHDRAW IN THE LAST SECOND.

OH, HEY, PEARL. IT'S OKAY. I DIDN'T TAKE A DIRECT HIT.

DIA!

DIA!

HUH ?!

WHO TOLD YOU TO DO THAT?

WHO ...

....

NOW HE CAN'T USE THE SECRETS OF THE MURALS FOR EVIL!

AND LAX FOUND AN OPENING TO SNATCH THE CAMERA FROM THAT MAN.

WHY DIDN'T YOU RIDE GARCHOMP WITH US LIKE I TOLD YOU TO?!

I TOLD YOU TO RUN AWAY!

WHO TOLD YOU TO DO A CRAZY THING LIKE THAT?!

ARE YOU STUPID, DIA?!

I'VE BEEN MEANING TO TELL YOU THIS FOR A WHILE, YOU KNOW...

YOU'RE ALWAYS BOSSING ME AROUND.

GRAB

BUT I THOUGHT IT WAS A BETTER IDEA FOR ME TO STAY— SO THAT'S WHAT I DID.

RUNNING AWAY WAS YOUR IDEA, PEARL.

MAYBE I AM.

...

PEARL, I'M NOT YOUR SIDEKICK!

...ARE YOU SAYING...?

WH-WHAT...

PEARL, I'M NOT YOUR SIDEKICK.

I'VE TAKEN A LOT OF GRIEF FROM YOU.

OUR STAND-UP COMEDY, OUR REHEARSALS, THE WAY YOU'RE ALWAYS HITTING ME IN OUR SLAPSTICK ROUTINE...

ALL THE TIME.

I BOSS YOU AROUND?! WHEN?!

AND I ONLY HIT YOU AS HARD AS I DO FOR THE GAG—TO MAKE IT FUNNIER!

...WHILE YOU'RE HANGING OUT EATING AND SLEEPING!

I WORK REALLY HARD TO COME UP WITH THAT STUFF—ALL ON MY OWN...

N-NOW HOLD ON! ARE YOU SAYING YOU DON'T LIKE THE ROUTINES I COME UP WITH?!

YOU SAY YOU DO IT FOR THE SHOW, FOR BOTH OF US— BUT IT'S REALLY JUST FOR YOU.

LIKE I SAID, YOU'RE BOSSY.

...ARE HAVING A FIGHT!

DIA-MOND AND PEARL...

...

KRUNCH

IT'S GETTING READY TO USE CHARGE BEAM!

HE'S COMING BACK TO GET HIS CAMERA!

GRAB

RUN AWAY!

DIA!

HAVE YOU FORGOTTEN OUR MISSION?!

WHY NO?!

NO!

WE'LL THROW THE CAMERA AS FAR AS WE CAN! WHILE HE'S CHASING AFTER IT, WE CAN GET AWAY.

STOP TALKING NONSENSE AND SAVE YOURSELF!

DIA! LISTEN TO ME!

...AND WE JUST GO AHEAD AND LET HIM...

IF HE USES THAT KNOWLEDGE FOR EVIL...

SOMEBODY JUST SAW A MURAL THAT NOBODY IS SUPPOSED TO SEE.

...FEELINGS...?

DIA'S...

TRAGEDY FOR ALL THE PEOPLE AND POKÉMON WHO LIVE HERE.

...IT CAN ONLY LEAD TO TRAGEDY.

I'VE NEVER SEEN DIA...

...SO MAD AND STUBBORN BEFORE!

LAX...

HE WON'T GIVE IT UP NO MATTER WHAT!

LAX IS HIDING THE CAMERA UNDER ITS LONG FUR!

100

UNLEASH THE MINI-NOSES...

... PROBO-PASS.

ZIP

ZIP

ZIP

WHOOSH

POP POP POP

BAM BAM BAM

AAA!

YOU WON'T BE ABLE TO FIND YOUR CAMERA IN THAT MESS.

I DON'T THINK IT EVEN REMEMBERS HOW MANY IT HAS!

LAX HAS LOTS OF BERRIES HIDDEN UNDER ITS LONG FUR.

MAGNE-ZONE...

HE'S USING MAGNETIC FORCE TO DRAW OUT HIS CAMERA!

EVEN MY POKÉ BALLS!

AND MINE!

MY POKÉ-DEX!

ANYTHING WITH METAL IN IT...IS GETTING PULLED TOWARDS HIM!

105

I NEVER CONSIDERED THEM.

DIA'S FEELINGS...

YOU'RE SHOWING ME WHAT REAL WILLPOWER IS, DIA.

I'M PRETTY... WEAK.

...ALL I CAN DO IS HELP HIM KEEP THAT CAMERA SAFE!

AND NOW...

THOOOM

GRAVITY! PRESS

PROBOPASS...

106

MY NAME IS CYRUS.

I SEEK A FORM OF ENERGY THAT WILL CREATE AN IDEAL WORLD— RID OF PETTY STRIFE.

MY HENCHMEN COULD LEARN A THING OR TWO FROM YOU.

I SEE YOU LISTEN TO YOUR HEART AND FOLLOW THROUGH WITH THE POWER OF YOUR WILL.

YOU'RE BOTH VERY BRAVE.

I'M QUITE IM-PRESS-ED.

FOR A POWER ONLY TOLD OF IN LEG-END?!

HOW ABOUT IT? WON'T YOU SEARCH WITH ME...?

ARE YOU ASKING US TO JOIN YOU...?

...

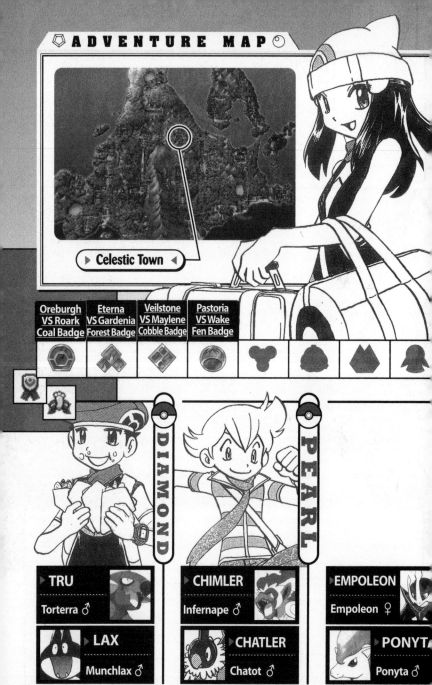

ADVENTURE MAP

▶ Celestic Town ◀

Oreburgh VS Roark Coal Badge	Eterna VS Gardenia Forest Badge	Veilstone VS Maylene Cobble Badge	Pastoria VS Wake Fen Badge				

DIAMOND

▶ TRU
Torterra ♂

▶ LAX
Munchlax ♂

PEARL

▶ CHIMLER
Infernape ♂

▶ CHATLER
Chatot ♂

▶ EMPOLEON
Empoleon ♀

▶ PONYTA
Ponyta ♂

33

Problematic
Probopass
& Mad
Magnezone
III

...TO YOUR ANSWER.

AND THIS IS MY ANSWER ...

A GROUND ATTACK COMBINED WITH AN ULTRA-STRONG MAGNETIC FORCE THAT DRAWS THE VERY MINERALS FROM THE GROUND!

OUR DEFIANCE WAS NOTHING COM- PARED TO THIS...

I CAN'T BELIEVE HE'S PULLING OUT ALL THE STOPS TO SHOW OFF HIS SUPERIOR POWER!

TEETER

TEETER

SKREECH

ZOOOM

OH, MY!

IT'S CLEAR-ING UP!

THE FOG...

AND PURE EMOTION.

AN UNYIELDING WILL.

...AND THE PICTURE IS COMPLETE.

ADD KNOWLEDGE TO THAT...

FOOSHH

VWEEEE

ZOOOOM

THAT'S THE DIF-FERENCE BETWEEN HIS PRES-ENCE AND HIS ABSENCE.

THE ATMO-SPHERE INSTANTLY TRANS-FORMED...

PHEW...

HE'S GONE—FINALLY!

LET'S JUST BE THANKFUL THAT WE'RE ALL OKAY.

AT LEAST... ...WE'RE TOGETH-ER.

I'M EVER SO THANK-FUL FOR YOUR HELP.

THANKS TO YOU, YOUNG MAN, HE DIDN'T TAKE ANY PICTURES OF THE WALL MURALS WITH HIM.

THAT BOY RISKED HIS LIFE TO STEAL THAT MAN'S CAMERA.

THAT'S NOT ALL...

...

YEAH! THAT'S MY DIA FOR YOU!

HUH...?

120

...THEY TOUCHED MY HEART!!

WHEN I CAUGHT A GLIMPSE OF THE DRAWINGS IN THE CAVE TODAY...

...THE ONES FACING EACH OTHER... HAD THE SAME EFFECT ON ME!!

THE DRAWINGS ON EITHER SIDE OF THE ENTRANCE...

AND THAT WASN'T ALL...!

I CAN ONLY SUPPOSE THEY WERE MADE TO TELL US SOMETHING VERY IMPORTANT!

THEY TOUCHED ME DEEPLY.

HE WAS COMMITTING THEM TO MEMORY.

OH ...

PERHAPS THEY'RE RELATED TO THE DRAWINGS INSIDE!

THAT MAN TOOK A LONG LOOK AT THEM BEFORE HE LEFT!

PLEASE, LADY! STOP!

I'D LIKE TO HELP GUARD THE MURALS TOO!

AAAGH!

IT'S UNSTABLE ENOUGH...

...WITHOUT YOU WHACKING THE TOWER LIKE THAT!

124

AND ZHEE WINDS, ZHEY CHANGE AND WE GET ALL—HOW YOU SAY—FOG-GEE!

I WAS VERY SURPRISE WHEN I SEE WHAT ZHIS FIGHT IS ALL ABOUT!

I WAS JUST PASSING THROUGH ON ZHEE PATROL.

YOU SAVED US! THANK YOU!

...PATROL?

OH, YES! PAS DU TOUT!

YOU SAW THE FIGHT?

066 Drifblim
Blimp Pokémon

Ghost | Flying

Height: 3' 11"
Weight: 33.1lbs

It carries people and Pokémon when it flies. But since it only drifts, it can end up anywhere.

YES, TERRIBLE...

BUT MY DRIFBLIM GOT SWEPT AWAY BY ZHEE WIND, PULLING ME FAR AWAY FROM IT! HA HA HA! QUE TERRIBLES, N'EST-CE PAS?

YOUR COMÉDIE ROUTINE!

URK!

NOW ZHAT WE ARE TOGETHER, I WOULD LIKE TO SEE IT AGAIN!

OH, MES AMIS!

SURE, FANTINA.

YOU'VE GOT BAD TIMING, FANTINA... DIA AND I JUST HAD THE BIGGEST FIGHT WE'VE EVER HAD SINCE WE BECAME A TEAM. NOTHING'S CLEAR ANYMORE...

IT IS ZHEE LEAST YOU COULD DO AFTER I HAVE SAVE YOU!

SPEAKING OF POKÉMON ...

SPEAKING OF POKÉMON ...

SO SPEAKING OF POKÉMON, THE FIRST THING THAT COMES TO MIND IS THAT IT'S A JOURNEY.

... THERE'S A LOT TO IT

BATTLING, TRAINING, EVOLVING, TRADING, HEALING, CATCHING, HATCHING...

I DON'T RECOGNIZE THIS ONE! IS HE AD-LIBBING?!

UH... SOME-THING, SOME-THING...

HE'S STARTING THE GAG HIM-SELF!

SPEAK-ING OF POKÉ-MON...

A JOURNEY OF THE SOUL.

BUT EVERY-BODY GOES ON SOME KIND OF JOURNEY.

I CAN'T PUT IT INTO WORDS.

AND, UH...

YOU LEARN ABOUT YOURSELF. AND OTHERS.

WHEN YOU GO ON ONE OF THESE TRIPS, JUST WATCH OUT THAT YOU DON'T **TRIP**!

THAT'S GOOD! YOU'RE ON THE RIGHT TRACK!

UH... UM... WHAT DO I SAY NOW?

AHAHA-HAHA!

TAKE CARE!

GOOD-BYE, GRAND-MA!

THANK YOU!

ADVENTURE MAP

▶Hearthome City◀

Oreburgh VS Roark Coal Badge	Eterna VS Gardenia Forest Badge	Veilstone VS Maylene Cobble Badge	Pastoria VS Wake Fen Badge				

DIAMOND

PEARL

▶ TRU
Torterra ♂

▶ LAX
Munchlax ♂

▶ CHIMLER
Infernape ♂

▶ CHATLER
Chatot ♂

▶ EMPOLEON
Empoleon ♀

▶ PONYTA
Ponyta ♂

34

Drifting
Drifblim

BZZT BZZT BZZT BZZT

THERE WE GO. NOW SHE'S RECOGNIZABLE.

... ODD THOUGH ...

ONE THING'S ...

HE WORKS FOR PROFESSOR ROWAN AND IS CURRENTLY ATTENDING A CONFERENCE IN CANALAVE CITY.

NOT ONLY RICH, BUT A FAMILY OF SCHOLARS. IN FACT, HER FATHER IS A POKÉMON RESEARCHER.

THE DAUGHTER OF THE BERLITZ FAMILY, THE RICHEST PEOPLE IN THE SINNOH REGION!

FWP FWP FWP FWP

VERY... ODD.

...LEAVING HER ALONE AND UNPROTECTED.

BUT NEITHER BODYGUARD WAS HEARD FROM AGAIN...

ON THE EVE OF HER DEPARTURE, HER FATHER ASSIGNED TWO BODYGUARDS TO PROTECT HER.

HIS DAUGHTER LEFT HOME AND WENT ON A JOURNEY.

HOWEVER...

I SUSPECT HIS DAUGHTER DIDN'T INFORM HIM THAT HER BODYGUARDS HAVE GONE MISSING.

HE SHOWS NO SIGNS OF DISTRESS, AND ATTENDS THE CONFERENCE SYMPOSIUMS DAILY.

...HER FATHER SEEMS UNPERTURBED.

...TO MAKE OUR MOVE.

THIS MIGHT BE A GOOD TIME...

...

...WE'VE BACK-TRACKED SO FAR WE'RE ALMOST WORSE OFF THAN BEFORE! WILL WE EVER GET TO CLIMB MT. CORONET?!

WE REALLY APPRECIATE YOU CATCHING US AND CARRYING US ON YOUR DRIFBLIM, BUT...

WE'RE RIGHT BACK WHERE WE STARTED!

H-HEARTHOME!

Pearl! Pull yourself together!

Are you speaking from zhee heart?!

Ah ha ha ha!

Thank you for the ride!

ACTUALLY, RETURNING TO HEARTHOME MIGHT NOT BE SO BAD.

OOH LA LA! WHAT A TRES BON IDEE! I WILL FIGHT YOU ANY DAY!

YES, NOW THAT WE'RE HERE! I WANT TO FIGHT *EVERY* GYM LEADER!

HUH?! YOU WANT TO FIGHT ANOTHER GYM BATTLE ALREADY?!

I HEAR THIS CITY HAS A GYM LEADER TOO—WHO I HAVEN'T CHALLENGED YET!

136

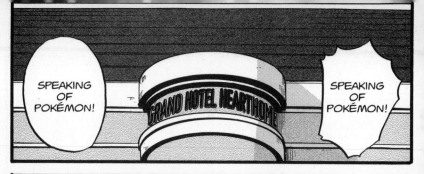

SPEAKING OF POKÉMON!

SPEAKING OF POKÉMON!

I'M TELLING YOU, SHE'S GOT A **FAT-INA** CHANCE OF WINNING!

THAT'S AWFULLY PESSIMISTIC.

I DON'T THINK LADY STANDS A CHANCE.

YEAH! LIKE THE ONE WE'RE ABOUT TO HAVE—AGAINST FANTINA.

THEY ENTER GYM BATTLES!

SLAP

THEN SHE'S **TOAST!**

...GHOST-TYPE POKÉMON!

HERE WE GO! FANTINA PREFERS TO USE...

THE OPPONENT'S POKÉMON TYPE IS...

LET'S BE OPTIMISTIC. WITH THE RIGHT STRATEGY, SHE MIGHT DEFEAT HER.

WHAT DO YOU MEAN?

BUT PERFORMERS NEED A WIDE REPERTOIRE!

I THINK WE'VE NAILED OUR STAND-UP ROUTINE AND PUNS.

TRUE. BUT DIAMOND... I HAVE A SUGGESTION.

NOT TOO SHABBY, I GUESS.

137

OKAY.

WE DON'T HAVE TO COME UP WITH ONE RIGHT NOW, BUT LET'S KEEP IT IN MIND—AS HOMEWORK.

IT'S A PERFORMER'S ULTIMATE WEAPON!

YES! FUNNI!! A. C'MON!

YEAH!

WE NEED A VISUAL GAG!

THUD THUD THUD

UM...

HM...

IF WE DO THAT, WE'LL NEED A LITTLE MORE...

HOW ABOUT THIS THEN?

HMM... SEEMS LIKE I'VE SEEN THAT BEFORE SOMEWHERE.

WHAT ABOUT THIS...?

SKILLED

HEY, LADY!

OKAY!

I'LL PRETEND I'M FANTINA SO SHE CAN PRACTICE ON ME.

DIA, I'M GONNA GO SEE LADY.

...

THUD THUD THUD

THANKS!

HELP YOU!

YOU'RE DOING GREAT! LET ME HELP YOU!

WELL...

WHAT STRATEGY DO YOU HAVE IN MIND?

AND LOOKING AT HER TRACK RECORD WITH OTHER CHALLENGERS, SHE CLINCHES HER WINS WITH MISMAGIUS. SO SHE'LL MOST LIKELY USE IT IN THIS BATTLE TOO.

...LIKE THE DRIFBLIM WE RODE ON.

ACCORDING TO MY RESEARCH, FANTINA USES GHOST-TYPE POKÉMON...

...WHAT CONCERNS ME IS THESE HALLUCINATIONS.

073 Mismagius
Magical Pokémon
Ghost
Height: 2' 11"
Weight: 9.7lbs

Its cries sound like incantations. Those who hear it are tormented by headaches and hallucinations.

ITS TYPE COMPATIBILITY AND STRENGTHS

WAIT RIGHT THERE!

ADD DIA'S LAX—AND CHOOSE A BATTLE IN WHICH YOU CAN SWITCH BETWEEN THE THREE OF THEM.

I KNOW!

OF COURSE I PLAN TO ENTER EMPOLEON AND PONYTA.

WHICH POKÉMON SHOULD I USE?

HOW WILL I DEFEND AGAINST THEM?

HOW WILL THAT FIGHT HALLUCINATIONS...?

VICTORY

A MUNCHLAX...

GYM

NEXT DAY...

140

141

YES, PROFESSOR ROWAN.

WE'RE ALMOST FINISHED GATHERING OUR MATERIALS.

Canalave City Pokémon Conference

UMM...

OH!

ASK THE STAFF FOR LOCAL RECOMMENDATIONS.

WE'VE BEEN VERY PRODUCTIVE. LET'S TREAT OURSELVES TO SOMETHING SWEET ON THE WAY BACK TO THE INN TODAY!

WE'RE IN THE FINAL STRETCH OF THIS LENGTHY CONFERENCE.

TUP-p

TUP-p

FWAP

TUP-p

TUP-p

TUP-p

THAT'S ALL RIGHT. I'LL WALK UP THE ROAD. YOU CAN CATCH UP.

EXCUSE ME, PROFESSOR. I LEFT SOMETHING BEHIND...

MR. BER- LITZ...

YOUR DAUGHTER... IS IT NOT?

TH- THAT'S ...!

...HAVE HER.

WE...

MY DAUGHTER IS ACCOM- PANIED BY EXCELLENT PROFES- SIONAL BODY- GUARDS!

PRE- POS- TER- OUS!

AND WE DEMAND 1.5 BIL- LION FOR HER SAFE RETURN.

NAH- AH-AH! DON'T TRY ANY FUNNY BUSI- NESS!

FLAP FLAP

TUP-P

TUP-P

YOU COULDN'T POSSIBLY HAVE PENETRATED THEIR FORCES AND KIDNAPPED HER.

I DON'T KNOW WHO YOU ARE, BUT YOU CAN'T FOOL ME!

IF YOU THINK I'M LYING...

TMP

...HA HA!

KYA HA HA...

I WOULD KNOW.

WE DISPOSED OF THEM.

...WHY DON'T YOU TRY GIVING THOSE PROFESSIONAL BODYGUARDS OF YOURS A CALL? I ASSURE YOU, THEY WON'T PICK UP.

⬠ ADVENTURE MAP ○

▶ Hearthome ◀

Oreburgh VS Roark oal Badge	Eterna VS Gardenia Forest Badge	Veilstone VS Maylene Cobble Badge	Pastoria VS Wake Fen Badge				

LADY

DIAMOND

PEARL

▶ TRU
Torterra ♂

▶ LAX
Munchlax ♂

▶ CHIMLER
Infernape ♂

▶ CHATLER
Chatot ♂

▶ EMPOLEON
Empoleon ♀

▶ PONYTA
Ponyta ♂

35

Mirages
of
Mismagius
I

...THEY ARE NO LONGER... ANYWHERE.

KYA HA HA! SO IF NEITHER OF THEM IS ANSWERING THAT CAN ONLY MEAN...

WATCH! THIS WAS...

...THE MOMENT OF THEIR DEMISE!

BZ Z Z Z ZT

BZZT   BZZT

KLATTER

YOU HAVE ONLY TO PAY US THE RANSOM AND WE WILL RELEASE HER AT ONCE.

SHE IS SAFE AND SOUND.

MY DAUGH-TER! IF YOU'VE HURT HER, I—

I TRUST THAT NOW I HAVE CON-VINCED YOU THAT YOUR DAUGHTER IS, IN FACT, IN OUR CUSTODY.

THAT WAS NO STAGED SPECIAL EFFECT.

TRMBL

TRMBL

IF YOU PICK THE DOOR THAT MATCHES THE CORRECT ANSWER...YOU CAN MOVE UP TO THE NEXT LEVEL. THAT PART, I GET. BUT...

THERE ARE THREE POSSIBLE ANSWERS FOR EACH PUZZLE AND THREE DOORS ON EACH FLOOR.

VWOOP

THERE'S THE LIFT! LADY, YOU GOT IT RIGHT AGAIN!

WELL, FANTINA SAYS SHE WAS A GOOD STUDENT...

WHY ARE ALL THE PUZZLES MATH PROBLEMS?!

BECOMING A GYM LEADER IS ABOUT **DIVIDING** YOURSELF FROM THE REST OF THE PACK AND **MULTIPLYING** YOUR TALENTS.

OH, IT'S THERE ALL RIGHT...

YEAH, BUT SHE STUDIED **POKÉMON**. WHERE'S THE DIVISION AND MULTIPLICATION IN THAT?

SO THIS MUST BE THE FOURTH FLOOR.

THAT MAKES FOUR PROBLEMS TOTAL.

HK

"C"!

THE NEXT ANSWER IS...

152

I HOPE LADY FEELS OKAY.

FEEL.... DIZZY AGAIN.

AND HER OPPONENT... LADY, 14 YEARS OF AGE...

MEET FANTINA, THE HEARTHOME GYM LEADER. ALSO KNOWN AS THE ALLURING, SOULFUL DANCER.

THIS WILL BE A SWITCH-IN BATTLE BETWEEN THREE POKÉMON!

...BEGIN!

LET THE BAT-TLE...

...

CALM DOWN, MISMA-GIUS. YOU WILL HAVE YOUR TURN.

MUNCH-LAX!

DUSKULL!

I KNOW JUST HOW TO USE IT IN THIS BATTLE!

THANKS AGAIN FOR LENDING ME YOUR MUNCHLAX, DIAMOND!

NOD

GIVE IT EVERYTHING YOU'VE GOT! HELP LADY WIN!

YOU CAN DO IT, LAX!

YOU CHOSE EACH ATTACK WISELY.

AND ZHEN USING BLIZZARD ON FLYING-TYPE DRIFBLIM...

USING ZHEE GHOST-TYPE MOVE LICK ON ZHEE GHOST-TYPE POKÉMON DUSKULL...

TRÉS BIEN, CHAL-LENGER.

ALLEZ, MISMA-GIUS! GO!

NOW THINGS WILL GET TRULY AMUSANT!

BOM

?!

UNH...

I FEEL DIZZY AGAIN...!

MUR MUR

MUR MUR

ZWOOP TWIST

WHAT ...?

!

THIS MUST BE MISMAGIUS'S HALLUCINATIONS!

GASP!

IMPOSSIBLE!

THE GYM JUST TURNED INTO A JUNGLE!

I- I'M TRYING!

THIS IS BAD, LADY! YOU BETTER WRAP THIS UP BEFORE THE HALLUCINATIONS GET THE BETTER OF YOU!

NOW I GET IT... THAT VERTIGO WE FELT WHEN WE GOT TO THE FOURTH FLOOR... IT WAS MISMAGIUS INFLUENCING US BEFORE THE MATCH EVEN BEGAN!

METAL CLAW!

SLAP

FWUMP

I THOUGHT FOR SURE WE'D WIN THROUGH SHEER SPEED!

OH, NO! MISMAGIUS'S ATTACK STRUCK BEFORE EMPOLEON'S!

FANTINA WAS USING THEM TO GAUGE LADY'S PERSONALITY! SINCE LADY IS GOOD AT SOLVING PROBLEMS WITH ONLY ONE CORRECT ANSWER, FANTINA MUST HAVE FIGURED THE HALLUCINATIONS WOULD WORK ESPECIALLY WELL ON HER!

YES...

SO **THAT'S** WHY ALL THE PUZZLES WERE MATH PROBLEMS!

PONYTA IS DONE FOR!

WHILE PONYTA WAS PANICK-ING...

...MISMA-GIUS HIT IT WITH A DARK PULSE!

THUD

...LEFT, NON?

ONE MORE...

36

Mirages
of
Mismagius
II

166

LAX TOTALLY FORGOT WE'RE IN THE MIDDLE OF A BATTLE!

LAX IS ALREADY LOST IN THAT IMAGINARY FEAST.

EASIER SAID THAN DONE...

STOP!

MAKE IT STOP!

G-GET A GRIP, LADY!

WATCH OUT, LAX, THAT'S...

RIGHT ON THE HEAD! DIA, WHAT DO WE DO NOW?! LAX IS IN TROUBLE!

...ENERGY BALL!

BLA

LIKE TRAINER, LIKE POKÉ-MON!

DIA'S RESPONDING THE SAME WAY. SIGH...

LADY ISN'T DOING SO WELL EITHER. HOW'S SHE SUPPOSED TO PLAN HER ATTACK IN THIS CONDITION?!

IT'S HARD TO FOCUS ON THE BATTLE-FIELD AT ALL!

UNGH. MY HEAD-ACHE IS GET-TING WORSE!

AND A TRAINER WHOSE HEAD HURTS TOO MUCH TO GIVE ORDERS...

A POKÉMON WHO'S TOO DISTRACTED TO FIGHT...

OOH, PEARL! THESE LOOK TASTY TOO!

H-HEY, DIA! HOLD ON!

BUT SHE'S NOT PUTTING HER PLAN INTO PRAC-TICE!

AND LADY WAS PREPARED TO COUN-TER-ATTACK.

...WITH HAL-LUCINA-TIONS.

WE KNEW THAT FANTINA USES HER MISMAGIUS TO CLINCH HER BATTLES...

I'VE GOT IT!

THE ATTACKS ARE MORE IN-TENSE THAN WE EX-PECTED!

WATCH OUT!!

DIA!

I'M EXPERIENCING THE SAME HALLUCINATION TOO... WHY IS MY RESPONSE SO DIFFERENT?

ACHE ACHE

HE'S SO... CAREFREE.

THE SAME ...?

HUH ...?

PEARL, YOU GOTTA TRY THIS!

MNCH MNCH MNCH MNCH MNCH

IT'S SO-O-O GOOD!

073 Mismagius
Magical Pokémon
Ghost
Height: 2'11"
Weight: 9.7lb

It chants incantations. While they usually torment targets, some chants bring happiness.

THERE'S AN INCANTATION THAT MAKES PEOPLE HAPPY!

THAT'S IT!

...THIS CRAZY SCENE MAKES HER HEAD SPIN—EVEN THOUGH SHE KNOWS IT'S JUST AN ILLUSION!

SAME FOR ME!

FOR LADY, WHO'S SO IN TOUCH WITH REALITY...

FOR SOME PEOPLE, THEY CAUSE HEADACHES! BUT FOR OTHERS, THEY MAKE THEM SO HAPPY THEY FORGET THEIR SURROUNDINGS AND PROBLEMS.

THE HALLUCINATIONS ARE THE SAME, BUT HOW YOU RESPOND TO THEM IS UP TO YOU!

FOR DIA...

BUT...

171

SO THEY'RE NOT IN ANY PAIN AT ALL!

LIKE LAX— HIS KINDRED SPIRIT.

SINCE HE LOVES TO EAT, DIA IS HAVING THE TIME OF HIS LIFE! THAT'S BECAUSE HE JUST ACCEPTS THE HALLUCINATION.

DASH

IT'S SO SIMPLE!

MUNCHLAX IS GETTING WEAKER ...

...WE FINISH IT OFF.

IT'S ABOUT TIME ...

AN ORDER... HAVE TO GIVE...AN ORDER...

OWW ...

Oh! Scrumptious!

MN CH

TLIP

SCAMPER

FOLLOW LAX'S LEAD.

KEEP IT UP, LADY!

THAT'S IT!

SHE WON! THE HALLUCINATION— IT DISAPPEARED!

THUD

!

DON'T YOU AGREE, SINNOH CHAIRMAN ...?

SO NOTHING PROHIBITED TOOK PLACE HERE.

ZHAT IS WHY I PERMITTED ZHEIR PRESENCE IN ZHEE FIRST PLACE!

BESIDES, SINCE ZHEE OBSERVERS WERE SUBJECT TO ZHEE HALLUCINATION ZHEMSELVES, ZHEY COULD NOT GIVE OBJECTIVE ADVICE.

ACK!

BY ZHEE WAY... WHERE DID ZHAT OTHER FUNNY BOY GO?

MY PLEASURE! I LOVE ZHEE YOUNG PEOPLE WHO WORK HARD AND ENTERTAIN ME! STUDY HARD—BUT LAUGH HARDER!

THANK YOU VERY MUCH, FANTINA.

I'VE GOT EVERYTHING... PERFECTLY... UNDER CONTROL...

DIA! ARE YOU OKAY?!

I'M FINE. STILL A BIT WOOZY THOUGH...

◈ A D V E N T U R E   M A P ○

►Hearthome City◄

Oreburgh VS Roark Coal Badge	Eterna VS Gardenia Forest Badge	Veilstone VS Maylene Cobble Badge	Pastoria VS Wake Fen Badge	Hearthome VS Fantina Relic Badge			

DIAMOND

PEARL

►TRU

Torterra ♂

►LAX

Munchlax ♂

►CHIMLER

Infernape ♂

►CHATLER

Chatot ♂

►EMPOLEON

Empoleon ♀

►PONYTA

Ponyta ♂

37

Brash
Bronzong
I

YOU MUST TRAVEL TO CANALAVE TOUT DE SUITE!

SACRE BLEU!

WE HAVE TO GO TO CANALAVE TO FIND YOUR DAD!

THIS IS NO TIME FOR MOUNTAIN CLIMBING!

WE'LL PUT OFF GOING TO MT. CORONET...

YES!

OF COURSE, LADY.

I AM SO SAD I CANNOT GO WITH YOU...

YOU HAD BEST RIDE ON MY DRIFBLIM AGAIN.

IT'S ALL RIGHT...

THANK YOU, FANTINA.

THIS IS MORE THAN ENOUGH HELP.

FLOAT

OTHER MEMBERS OF HER FAMILY MIGHT SHOW UP TOO.

WE'RE GOING TO THE PLACE WHERE LADY'S FATHER WAS KIDNAPPED...

I WILL HOPE FOR YOUR *PÈRE'S* SAFE RETURN!

AND IF THEY ARE...

...OF DIA AND ME?!

...WHAT WILL THEY THINK...

HOW WILL THEY FEEL ABOUT THAT?!

WE'RE NOT HER **REAL** BODYGUARDS— BUT WE'RE ESCORTING HER.

...ARE YOU SURE THIS IS A GOOD IDEA? WE HAVE TO HELP LADY, BUT...

HEY, PEARL!

WE CAN WORRY ABOUT THE BODYGUARD PROBLEM AFTER WE GET THERE.

WE HAVE TO GO TO CANALAVE WITH LADY. WE DON'T HAVE A CHOICE.

BUT...

I'D BE LYING IF I SAID I WASN'T WOR-RIED.

THE CANA-LAVE LI-BRARY!

AND THERE'S WHERE THEY HELD THE POKÉMON CONFER-ENCE...

CANA-LAVE CITY...

WE'RE HERE!

IT'S SO EARLY. NOBODY'S HERE.

THERE...

KEEP OUT KEEP OUT KEEP OUT KEEP OUT KEEP OUT KEEP OUT KEEP OUT KEEP OUT KEEP OUT KEEP OUT KEEP OUT

OF COURSE THEY WOULD RESTRICT ACCESS AFTER...YOU KNOW.

...AND PROFESSOR ROWAN WERE...

THIS IS WHERE MY FATHER...

I THINK WE SHOULD FIND AN INN AND GET SOME REST.

WHAT SHOULD WE DO NOW, LADY?

LADY...

190

H-HEY!

ARE YOU SURE IT WAS YOUR DAD'S VOICE?

THAT VOICE YOU HEARD... IT CAME FROM THIS BUILDING?!

LADY! YOU CAN'T JUST BARGE INTO PLACES!

WHO ARE YOU PEOPLE?

THAT'S WHAT I'D LIKE TO KNOW!

HUH? WHO?

THERE'S SOME- ONE HERE!

GO AHEAD. TRY TO TAKE ME ON!

...I DOUBT YOU'RE UP TO ANYTHING GOOD!

SINCE YOU'RE WALTZING IN HERE AT THE CRACK OF DAWN WITHOUT PERMISSION...

OH...

MEAN- WHILE, IN ORE- BURGH CITY...

VROOOM

WOW! HOW LONG HAS IT BEEN SINCE WE SAW THEM?

WITH HIS CRANIDOS.

IT'S THE OREBURGH CITY GYM LEADER, ROARK.

LOOK THERE, YELLOW!

ZIP ZIP ZIP

TRMBL

TRMBL

OH! OH! OH!

OH...

195

SHAAA

YOU REALLY ARE NOTHING LIKE YOUR OLD MAN BYRON. HE'S SUCH A MESS—OH! I'M SORRY!

WOULDN'T EXPECT ANYTHING LESS FROM HIM. SO PERCEPTIVE...

ROARK KNOWS WHEN HIS POKÉMON ARE GOING TO EVOLVE.

DID YOU HEAR THAT, YELLOW?

HEY THERE.

OH, WOW! IT EVOLVED! WELL DONE, ROARK!

YEP. JUST LIKE I PREDICTED.

A FEW WEEKS AGO, DIDN'T YOU SAY YOUR DAD CALLED AND ASKED YOU TO COME TO CANALAVE?

BY THE WAY, ROARK...

YEP, THAT'S RIGHT!

BUT HE DOES HAVE AN INCREDIBLE SIXTH SENSE.

NAH, IT'S TRUE. MY FATHER IS TOTALLY SPACY.

SOME-THING WAS BOTH-ERING HIM...

...

WHAT FOR? I KNOW IT'S NONE OF MY BUSINESS, BUT... I'M CURIOUS.

MY FATHER TOOK IT UPON HIMSELF TO INVESTIGATE THE GANG, AND THEN...

"STRANGE ACTIVITY"...?

HE WANTED TO KNOW WHAT I THOUGHT OF SOME STRANGE ACTIVITY GOING ON AT CANALAVE.

THEY DIDN'T DO ANYTHING BAD EXACTLY, BUT... THEY'VE BEEN RESEARCHING ANCIENT ARCHIVES IN THE LIBRARY.

A SUSPICIOUS GANG KEPT VISITING THE CITY.

197

I'VE GOT A BAD FEELING ABOUT THIS...

WELL, I'LL BE!

TWO RESEARCHERS ATTENDING THE POKÉMON CONFERENCE WENT MISSING...

...THIS HAPPENED.

IN-DEED.

HOW ODD.

IT SEEMS YOUR FATHER WAS RIGHT ABOUT TROUBLE BREWING...

SHE FOUND YELLOW WANDERING AIMLESSLY AROUND ROUTE 210...

A NICE PERSON BROUGHT YELLOW BACK TO ME.

HM. YOU KNOW, YELLOW WAS MISSING FOR A WEEK...

HE'S KNOWN TO RUSH HEADLONG INTO THINGS.

BUT... AT TIMES LIKE THIS, MY DAD OFTEN ACTS RASHLY.

THAT WAY HIS PAYBACK ATTACK WOULD BE TWICE AS STRONG!

HE LET IT HIT—SO HE COULD SET UP HIS COUNTER-ATTACK!

AND NOT JUST IN TERMS OF TYPE ADVANTAGES. THE AQUA JET LADY JUST UNLEASHED IS AN ATTACK THAT ALWAYS STRIKES FIRST!

HE'S STRONG!

LADY ...!?

PLEASE STAY OUT OF THIS!

BOM BOM BOM

DIA, WE BETTER STOP HER!

I DON'T CARE IF I HAVE TO USE FORCE!

I'LL MAKE HIM CON-FESS!

AND SINCE THIS MAN ATTACKED US THE MOMENT HE SAW US— I CAN'T HELP BUT THINK HE HAS SOME-THING TO DO WITH IT!

I'M POSITIVE I HEARD MY FATHER'S VOICE EMANATING FROM THIS BUILDING!

JOSH

Message from
Hidenori Kusaka

Cyrus is the mysterious creepy archvillain of the *Pokémon Adventures* series. This first direct confrontation between Cyrus and our trio of heroes is the highlight of this volume! Despite their fears, they face him with their heads held high. Hope you enjoy the story!

Message from
Satoshi Yamamoto

I bet the preview in the last volume worried a lot of readers. So far, best friends Diamond and Pearl have been the perfect team...but now they're fighting! And what will happen to Lady? The bonds between our three friends will be sorely tested in volume 4 as we reach the climax of the Diamond and Pearl story arc!

More Adventures Coming Soon...

Lady feels betrayed when she finally discovers the truth about Diamond's and Pearl's identities. Is the trio's journey—and friendship—over?! And how can our three heroes save three Legendary Lake Pokémon from Team Galactic... when each Legendary Pokémon is in a *different lake*?!

Meanwhile, what is Team Galactic secretly manufacturing in an abandoned factory...?

Plus, meet Shieldon, Gliscor, Lucario, Vespiquen and many more Sinnoh Pokémon friends!

FOLLOW PIPLUP AND READ THIS MANGA FROM RIGHT TO LEFT!

THIS IS THE END OF THIS GRAPHIC NOVEL!

To properly enjoy this VIZ Media graphic novel, please turn it around and begin reading from right to left.

This book has been printed in the original Japanese format in order to preserve the orientation of the original artwork. Have fun with it!

follow the action this way